Contents

C000147749

Fronted adverbials: words and phrases

Adverbials add detail about when, where, how or why things happen. Adverbials can be single words (adverbs) or phrases. You can choose to put an adverbial at the start (or front) of a sentence. This is called a **fronted adverbial**, and should be followed by a **comma**.

Usually, Tyler hated getting up in the morning.
In a faraway land, on a distant hillside,
beside a trickling stream, there stood a cottage.

Try it

1 Underline the **adverbials** in these sentences.

Frantically, he searched the beach beneath the cliffs.

On the stroke of half time, United scored in front of their excited fans.

With the help of our keen volunteers, the wildlife garden will soon be open.

Inside the restaurant, the fire in the grate flickered with a warming glow.

Across the country, from town to town, from street to street, the news spread.

With a pencil, make a mark in the middle of the circle.

2 Add at least <u>one</u> **adverbial** to the start of each sentence. Use the correct **punctuation**.

_____ we heard a cry.

_____ the dog spoke to him.

_____ the old car rattled down the road.

_____ Archie followed the man with the tall hat.

_____ there lived a wise man.

Sentence practice

Write the opening sentence for a story, starting with at least <u>one</u> **adverbial**.

_____

_____

Fronted adverbials: clauses

Remember

Subordinate clauses start with a **conjunction** and function as **adverbials**. Subordinate clauses tell you more about the event in the **main clause**. You can put the subordinate clause before the main clause. These fronted subordinate clauses, like other fronted adverbials, are followed by a **comma**.

<u>As the lightning lit up the night,</u> she saw a figure in the doorway.
<u>Although it was just a glimpse,</u> Abbie thought it was him.

Try it

1 Underline the **subordinate clause** in each sentence. Circle the **conjunction**.

Although it was raining, the air was still warm.

In the morning, he gave her a map so that she could find her way.

Once we have the money, we will buy new equipment for the gym.

Whenever I leave the room, you start misbehaving.

Since it was time for lunch, she ran home.

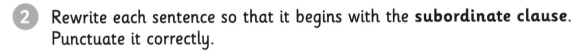

2 Rewrite each sentence so that it begins with the **subordinate clause**. Punctuate it correctly.

The visitor paused for a moment before he spoke to the class.

_____

George could not rest while his father was in danger.

_____

The children climbed over the fence although they weren't really allowed in the garden.

_____

_____

Sentence practice

Write <u>three</u> sentences using the **main clause** below. Start each sentence with a different **subordinate clause**.

… she went through the gate.

_____

_____

_____

Punctuating direct speech

In **direct speech**, the spoken words are sometimes split up, with 'said X' in the middle of them. If someone says two complete sentences, you put a full stop between the sentences.

"It sounds like rats," said Dylan. "There are probably hundreds of them down there."

If someone says one sentence, you put a comma after 'said X' to show that the sentence continues.

"I heard it before," said Maya, "but this time it's louder."

Try it

1 Read this **direct speech** and decide if there is <u>one</u> spoken sentence or <u>two</u>. Then add the missing **punctuation**.

Take care of yourself she shouted Those roads can be dangerous

We must find the wise man said the chief and ask him what to do

You stay here said Arjun while we go inside

It's not my fault Natalie said quickly I was only trying to help

You should hurry said the ticket inspector because the train is leaving

in a few minutes

2 Complete the sentence spoken by each character and add the **punctuation**.

I'm having a party announced Kayla and _____

I've looked everywhere moaned Louie but _____

When it stops raining said Sarah _____

We are going to the cinema explained Lucy so _____

We should stay here insisted Nisha or _____

Sentence practice

Freya and Lee are trapped. Write <u>two</u> lines of **direct speech**, split up as above, to show this.

_____

_____

Direct and indirect speech

Direct speech records the actual words that are spoken, by putting them in **inverted commas**.

Megan said, "I can't come."

Indirect speech (also called **reported speech**) records what has been said without using the actual words spoken. No inverted commas are needed.

Megan said that she couldn't come.

Try it

1 Write whether each sentence shows **direct speech** or **indirect speech**. If it is direct speech, add the missing **punctuation**.

She said that she hated singing in assembly. _____

Jason shouted Let's get out of here! _____

Bella told us that the hall was flooded. _____

Elijah agreed that we were right. _____

Mum sighed I think that is a very bad idea. _____

2 Complete the boxes so that each sentence is written as **direct speech** and then as **indirect speech**. Punctuate your answers correctly.

Direct speech	Indirect speech
Mrs Shah said, "Everyone go home."	
	He shouted to us to follow the car.
	She asked if we were busy.
"You can help if you want to," said Dad.	

Sentence practice

Ross tells his mum that he is going to Amit's house. Write his mum's reply using **indirect speech**.

Pronouns

There are many different types of **pronoun** but they all have the same function – they stand in place of **nouns** or noun phrases.

<u>A man</u> was walking along when he saw something on the ground – <u>a handful of sparkling beads</u>. He picked them up. "Well, look at these," he said to himself. "Someone must have dropped them."

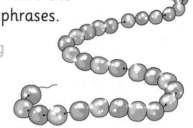

Try it

1 Underline all the **pronouns** in each sentence.

Mum made herself a cup of tea and poured us some juice.

Rose ran away when she heard something moving in the woods.

That ice cream looks delicious. Can I have some?

We organised the event ourselves and it was a great success.

They looked at all the paintings and decided mine was the best.

If you give her the seeds, Lucia can plant them herself.

2 Rewrite each sentence using **pronouns** instead of the underlined nouns and noun phrases.

<u>This workbook</u> is <u>your workbook</u> and <u>that workbook</u> is <u>my workbook</u>.

_____

<u>Scott</u> was annoyed with <u>Scott</u> when <u>Scott</u> missed <u>the open goal</u>.

_____

<u>An unknown person</u> was coming so <u>Anish and I</u> hastily put <u>the letters</u> back.

_____

Sentence practice

Write a sentence using the **pronouns** 'someone' and 'himself'.

_____

_____

Pronouns and ambiguity

You can use **pronouns** to avoid repeating **nouns** or noun phrases. However, it must be clear which noun or noun phrase a pronoun refers to.

When Aaron rode <u>his bike</u> into <u>the fence</u>, he badly damaged it. (meaning is unclear or ambiguous)
Aaron badly damaged <u>his bike</u> when he rode it into <u>the fence</u>. (meaning is clear)

Try it

1 Which <u>two</u> **nouns** could the underlined **pronoun** in each sentence refer to?

If I take the model off the stand, it will be easier to mend <u>it</u>.

_____ or _____

When the hunters went to catch the stags, <u>they</u> ran away.

_____ or _____

When Dad dropped the computer on his leg, <u>it</u> broke.

_____ or _____

I saw her picture in a magazine but now I can't find <u>it</u>.

_____ or _____

The police told the passengers that <u>they</u> would be there for some time.

_____ or _____

2 Now rewrite the sentences above, keeping the **pronoun** but making clear which **noun** it refers to.

_____

_____

_____

_____

_____

Sentence practice

Write a sentence using the **nouns** 'rabbit' and 'hat' and the **pronoun** 'it'.

_____

Verbs: auxiliary verbs

Remember

Verbs have two **tenses**: past and present. Other **verb forms** are made by putting 'helper' verbs before the main verb. These helper verbs are called **auxiliary verbs**.

United <u>have been</u> woeful recently.   (perfect form)
Johnson <u>was waiting</u> at the far post.   (progressive form)
United <u>will face</u> City in the next round.   (future time)

Try it

1   Add the **auxiliary verb** needed to complete each sentence.

The girl _____ fidgeting in her seat all through the show.

We _____ chosen a name for our new puppy.

Dominic _____ known Becky for years.

There _____ be a full moon tonight.

It is late but the children _____ still searching for the lost tortoise.

I _____ not want gravy on my broccoli.

2   Rewrite each sentence using the **auxiliary verb** shown in brackets.

He explained it all to me.   _____ (has)

I wrote a story about you.   _____ (have)

Her hands trembled.   _____ (were)

I listen to the music.   _____ (am)

They are singing here today.   _____ (will)

I like tea but not coffee.   _____ (do)

Sentence practice

Write <u>two</u> different sentences using the verb 'beat' with the **auxiliary verb** 'have/has'.

_____

_____

Verbs: perfect forms

Remember

The **present perfect form** uses the auxiliary verb 'has' or 'have' before the main verb. It is used to write about events that have happened in the recent past, are still ongoing or have consequences now. The **past perfect form** uses the auxiliary verb 'had' to show that one event happened before another past event.

Joe <u>has become</u> a successful businessman.   (present perfect)
Once Joe <u>had learnt</u> to drive, he got a job.   (past perfect)

Try it

1. Underline the **past perfect form** of **verbs** in these sentences.

   The farmer had been outside chopping wood before he began to build the fire.

   Once Dalia had finished her chores, she sat down for a rest.

   The coach was pleased because the players had done their best.

   I wanted to see Miss Braithwaite but she had gone for lunch.

   Amber stared at the boy because she was sure she had seen him before.

   Charlie was excited because he had wanted to visit Japan for a long time.

2. Rewrite each sentence using the **present perfect verb form** rather than the simple past tense.

   The house <u>was</u> empty for months.   _____

   I <u>forgot</u> my password.   _____

   Rewrite each sentence using the **past perfect verb form** rather than the simple past tense.

   I <u>finished</u> all my homework.   _____

   He <u>gave</u> away all his money.   _____

Sentence practice

Add <u>two</u> sentences about what had happened, using **past perfect verb forms**.

Kyle sat down and cried. It had been a disastrous day. _____

_____

Standard English

Remember

Non-Standard English is sometimes used in speech, but in writing you should nearly always use Standard English. Pay attention to pronouns and verb forms, as these are often confused.

Sam and me was always playing in the park.
Them was great days.   (non-Standard English)
Sam and I were always playing in the park.
Those were great days.   (Standard English)

Try it

1 Add the correct word to complete each sentence using **Standard English**.

On Friday morning, Joseph and _____ tidied the art cupboard.   (me I)

We decided to stack _____ boxes on top of each other.   (them those)

It was a funny story _____ he told us.   (what that)

I need _____ glasses to read the newspaper.   (my me)

Mrs Hawkins sent Jude and _____ to fetch the register.   (me I)

There is a lot of wildlife living in _____ woods.   (them those)

2 Rewrite each sentence using **Standard English**.

Me and me dad have writ to the council about them bins left outside our house.

_____

I think them computer games what you wanted is in me bedroom.

_____

It were so windy that it blowed me hat off me head and into them bushes over there.

_____

_____

Sentence practice

Write a sentence using **non-Standard English**. Then rewrite it using Standard English.

_____

_____

Standard English: double negatives

Remember

Negative words, including 'no', 'nothing', 'never' and 'not' (also written as the contraction –n't), are used in negative sentences. You only need <u>one</u> negative word in a sentence. If you use two negative words, they cancel each other out and the sentence means the opposite of what was intended.

I didn't see nobody.   ✗   (double negative)

I didn't see anybody. or I saw nobody.   ✓   (Standard English)

Try it

1 Add the correct word to complete each sentence using **Standard English**.

Max never told _____ about the argument.   (anybody nobody)

You're not going _____ until you've finished. (nowhere anywhere)

I've never seen _____ like it before.   (anything nothing)

Vasanth didn't have _____ brothers or sisters.   (no any)

I'm not going to play tennis _____ again.   (never ever)

Jenny couldn't find _____ work at the factory.   (no any)

2 Rewrite these sentences so that the meaning is clear.

I don't want no sugar in my tea.   _____

I'm not going nowhere this morning.   _____

I don't know nothing about computers.   _____

Holly's not talking to nobody today.   _____

I never saw no lorry outside.   _____

I don't trust none of them.   _____

Sentence practice

Write <u>three</u> sentences using **negative** words to give warnings. Remember to avoid double negatives.

_____

_____

_____

Revision 1

1 Insert **commas** in the correct places in these sentences.

Butterflies dragonflies mosquitoes gnats and moths are all examples of flying insects.

A spacious living room modern kitchen and large dining room can all be found on the ground floor.

Ripe mangoes figs sweet potatoes colourful fabrics and shiny trinkets were just some of the things on sale at the market.

Mowing the lawn raking up the leaves and planting the bulbs are some of the jobs I must do in the garden this weekend.

2 Rewrite the phrases below using an **apostrophe** to show **possession**.

the neck of a giraffe   _____

the nest belonging to the ants   _____

the playground for children   _____

the settlement of the invaders   _____

3 Add a **question tag** to make each statement into a question. Punctuate it correctly.

It's Monday today_____

Mel likes strawberries_____

We should wait for Owen_____

You collect football programmes_____

4 One word in the sentence below uses an **apostrophe** incorrectly. Underline the word.

Mrs Neil's pupils stacked their chair's by the classroom door.

Explain why it is incorrect.

_____

_____

_____

5 Use a different **co-ordinating conjunction** to add another **clause** to each sentence below.

Robbie's alarm clock began to bleep

_____

Robbie's mum always had to shake him

_____

Robbie turned his pillow over

_____

6 Complete each sentence with a different **possessive pronoun**.

This is _____

That is _____

These are _____

Those are _____

7 Rewrite the sentence below by moving an **adverbial** to the start of the sentence. Punctuate the new sentence correctly.

I sat down and replied to her letter immediately after lunch.

_____

8 Underline the **main clause** in each sentence.

There was a crash as the man fell over.

Once Leo had found the address, he set off down the road.

Nikesh crossed the track so that he could read the sign.

Just as Bethany was about to step out of the front door, she heard a strange noise.

9 Rewrite the sentence below, adding a **subordinate clause**.

The people screamed.

_____

10 Label the boxes to show the **word class** each word belongs to.

She   gave   a   friendly   smile.

Writing task 1

What an adventure!

"Don't press the button," said a voice.

An adventure story starts with these words. Your task is to write the opening of this adventure story. You should describe the events that follow after the opening line.

Before you start writing, think about:

- where the story takes place
- who the characters are
- what happens next
- how to make the story exciting

Use this space to write down some ideas.

Remember

- Think about the grammar and vocabulary you use.
- Use correct punctuation.
- Check your work carefully.

What an adventure!

"Don't press the button," said a voice. _____

_____

_____

_____

_____

_____

_____

_____

_____

_____

_____

_____

_____

_____

_____

_____

_____

_____

_____

_____

_____

_____

Determiners

A **determiner** is the word that comes before a **noun** or at the start of a noun phrase. Many different types of words can be used as determiners. They can tell you whether the noun is known or unknown.

the report	this school	our pupils	two schemes	(known)
a car	an idea	some parents	many children	(unknown)

Try it

1 Underline all the **determiners** in each sentence.

Some new houses are cramped but this house has a spacious living room.

Every magnet has two poles, a north pole and a south pole.

The room was small, with one window overlooking her little garden.

Most lizards have four legs but some, such as the slow-worm, have no legs.

All bats in this country are protected by the law.

It took many weeks and much effort for those brave explorers to reach the North Pole.

2 Complete each sentence using suitable **determiners**.

_____ metals are hard but _____ metals are softer and more flexible.

_____ mole uses _____ front feet to loosen _____ earth when it is digging.

Behind us, there was _____ empty space with _____ trees in the middle but _____ grass.

_____ seagulls just swooped down for _____ crumbs left from _____ sandwiches.

_____ animals such as _____ chameleon can change _____ colour to match _____ background.

Sentence practice

Write a sentence about a puppy, using <u>three</u> different **determiners**.

_____

Expanded noun phrases

Remember

You can add words and phrases to **nouns** to form expanded **noun phrases**. These help to give more information about the noun. An expanded noun phrase might include a **determiner**, one or more **adjectives**, other nouns and/or **prepositional phrases**.

squirrel → the squirrel → the grey squirrel → the graceful grey squirrel → the graceful grey tree squirrel with a long bushy tail

Try it

1 Underline the expanded **noun phrase** built around each **noun** in **bold**.

The biologist gave a very interesting **talk** about unusual animals.

A green grass **snake** with small black markings slithered into view.

We visited several interesting ancient **monuments** while on holiday in Italy.

Deer have branched **antlers** with a velvety covering.

From his balcony, he could look out over the golden **roofs** of the city.

I tried to count the glittering **stars** in the sapphire sky.

2 Rewrite each sentence using an expanded **noun phrase**.

We sell hats.

I came to a door.

Once there was a cat.

This is a butterfly.

Sentence practice

Write a sentence about an elaborate feast. Use <u>three</u> expanded **noun phrases**.

Relative clauses 1

You can use a **relative clause** to give more information about a **noun** mentioned in a sentence. A relative clause usually begins with a **relative pronoun**, such as 'who', 'which', 'that' or 'whose'.

Once, there was a poor king <u>who had a threadbare cloak</u>.
The crown <u>that he wore</u> was made of tin.

In some relative clauses the relative pronoun is missed out.
The crown <u>~~that~~ he wore</u> was made of tin.

Try it

1 Underline the **relative clause** in each sentence. Circle the **relative pronoun**.

Mum has a friend who works at the hospital.

She came to the old brick wall, which ran round the side of the house.

The fish had silver scales that glittered red and gold.

The robins that we see in the garden are quite tame.

We spoke to the man whose house was struck by lightning.

We would like to thank everyone who helped us with our bake sale.

2 Complete each **relative clause** to give information about the **noun**.

I sent an email to my friend who _____

She climbed down the rope that _____

I met an old man whose _____

I read the book, which _____

He told us about his daughter who _____

She picked up the shovel that _____

Sentence practice

Write an interesting fact about a teacher, using a **relative clause**.

_____

Relative clauses 2

A **relative clause** tells you more about a **noun**. Some relative clauses begin with 'where' or 'when'. You use 'where' to refer to places and 'when' to refer to times.

At the end of the street, there was a house <u>where no-one ever went</u>.

Try it

1 Use the words 'where' or 'when' to complete the **relative clause** in each sentence.

It was a long walk back to the caravan park _____ we were staying.

1969 was the year _____ man first landed on the moon.

We go swimming at the leisure centre _____ my mother works.

Today is the day _____ our cousins arrive back from Greece.

March is the month _____ the daffodils start to grow in my aunt's garden.

Visit the town of Stratford-upon-Avon _____ Shakespeare was born.

2 Rewrite each sentence using a **relative clause** to add the information shown in brackets.

It was Monday afternoon.   (The hurricane struck on Monday afternoon.)

_____

This is New Street Station.   (We catch the train to London from New Street Station.)

_____

There is still a stain on the carpet.   (Dad dropped a tin of paint on the carpet.)

_____

Sentence practice

Complete this sentence using a **relative clause**.

I remember the day _____

Parenthesis: brackets

Remember

Sometimes extra detail is added into a sentence. This may be something interesting but not essential to the sentence's meaning. You use <u>two</u> **brackets** to clearly separate the extra information (or **parenthesis**) from the main sentence.

Jesse Owens (<u>an American athlete</u>) won four gold medals at the 1936 Olympics.

Try it

1 Underline the extra information (**parenthesis**) that has been added in each sentence. Then insert the missing **brackets**.

Mrs Bahra our neighbour is always watching us from her window.

For breakfast, there was scrambled egg which I hate or porridge.

The tower built in 1853 will soon be open to the public again.

The giant panda which lives in China is extremely rare.

Charles Dickens 1812–1870 was a famous and popular writer.

We spoke to Mr Cooper the school's head teacher about the building work.

2 Rewrite each sentence using **brackets** to add a **parenthesis** where shown by the arrow.

↓
Grandma's dogs travel everywhere with her.

_____

↓
Jack was the first to complete the puzzle.

_____

↓
This book is my favourite story of all time.

_____

Sentence practice

Write <u>two</u> sentences about a member of your family. Use **brackets** to add a **parenthesis** to each sentence.

_____

_____

Parenthesis: commas and dashes

Remember

You can use <u>two</u> **commas** or <u>two</u> **dashes** instead of brackets to show a **parenthesis** in a sentence. As with brackets, the dashes or commas clearly separate the extra information from the main sentence.

Jamie's mother, <u>who was a great cook</u>, had been baking all day. The cakes – <u>all ten of them</u> – had vanished!

Try it

1 Rewrite each sentence using **dashes** or **commas** to separate the extra information (the **parenthesis**) from the main sentence.

The Moon although it appears to be silver actually has no light.

_____

Jamila's father who is a doctor told us about his work at the hospital.

_____

_____

The water was cold really freezing so we quickly jumped out again.

_____

They threw everything bills, letters and notes into the bin.

_____

2 Add a **parenthesis** into the sentence. Use **commas** or **dashes** to punctuate it.

The city _____ was an exciting place to be.

Mars _____ is smaller than Earth.

Gavin _____ won the competition.

The casket _____ is now on display in the museum.

Sentence practice

Write a sentence about a messy ice cream, including a **parenthesis**. Use **commas** or **dashes** to punctuate it.

_____

_____

Adverbs and possibility

Remember

Adverbs can be used when discussing possibilities. The adverbs can suggest different levels of certainty. Some adverbs make ideas sound certain, while others make them sound less sure.

That is definitely the best idea. We clearly can't stay here.   (certain)
Perhaps ... but maybe we should wait.   (less certain)

Try it

1 Underline the **adverb** in each sentence. Then tick any sentences with adverbs that show certainty.

The bad weather possibly caused the accident.

I will certainly arrive before the party ends.

I think I could probably swim across the river.

Surely, this will solve the problem.

He was obviously the best singer in the competition.

Perhaps, we will go on holiday in July.

2 Rewrite each sentence using an **adverb** to make it sound more certain.

The new machine will work. _____

This answer is wrong. _____

I think this is the best book. _____

Rewrite each sentence using an adverb to make it sound less certain.

We will win the lottery. _____

This will cheer you up. _____

I could be there by two o'clock. _____

Sentence practice

Write <u>two</u> sentences about why a boy is waving at you, using **adverbs** to show different levels of possibility.

_____

_____

Modal verbs and possibility

Remember

Modal verbs are used with other verbs to show different levels of possibility. They can make statements sound certain or more like a possibility.

Today will be a good day.   (certain)
This afternoon I could go swimming. (possible)

Try it

1 Underline the **modal verb** in each sentence. Write whether the modal verb makes it sound **certain** or **possible**.

We can get to the top of this mountain.   _____

This bridge could collapse at any moment.   _____

We must take some sun cream to the beach.   _____

There may be a storm overnight.   _____

The hero might save the villagers from the
fearsome ogre.   _____

You will love the new track from this
popular band.   _____

2 Rewrite each sentence using a different **modal verb** to change the meaning.

He <u>can</u> finish the race.   _____

We <u>should</u> raise enough money.   _____

You <u>could</u> ask an adult to help you. _____

I <u>might</u> have cereal for breakfast. _____

Sophie <u>might</u> swim 50 metres.   _____

I <u>must</u> throw a six this time.   _____

Sentence practice

Write <u>three</u> sentences about the future, using **modal verbs** to show different levels of possibility.

_____

_____

_____

Verbs with suffixes

Some **verbs** are formed from **nouns** or **adjectives** by adding **suffixes** (such as –ify, –ise, –en, –ate) to the **root words**. Sometimes the root word has to change its spelling.

solid → solid<u>ify</u>   hard → hard<u>en</u>

category → categor<u>ise</u>   vap<u>our</u> → evap<u>or</u>ate

Try it

1 Add a **suffix** to each noun or adjective to make a **verb**. Write the verb.

simple   _____   straight   _____

medic   _____   pressure   _____

pure   _____   electric   _____

captive   _____   light   _____

flat   _____   active   _____

computer   _____   equal   _____

2 Complete each sentence with a **verb** formed from a noun or adjective in the box.

   note   hard   critic   terror   strength   sympathy

Exercise will _____ your muscles.

I find it hard to _____ someone else's work.

The cement will _____ as it dries out.

Some of the rides at theme parks _____ me.

Please _____ the head teacher if your child is ill.

I can _____ with your point of view.

Sentence practice

Write a sentence using **verbs** formed by adding **suffixes** to the words 'energy' and 'strength'.

_____

_____

Verbs with prefixes

Remember

When a **prefix** such as dis–, mis–, over–, re–, or de– is added to the beginning of a **verb**, it changes the meaning of the verb.

load
reload   (load it again)
overload (load it too much)

Try it

1 Add a **prefix** to each **verb** to change its meaning. Then write the meaning of the new verb.

_____behave   means _____

_____flow   means _____

_____continue means _____

_____consider means _____

_____calculate means _____

_____pay   means _____

2 Complete each sentence. Use the underlined **verb** again but change the **prefix**.

The magician <u>disappeared</u> but _____

Simply <u>inflate</u> the bouncy castle and _____

Some shops <u>undercharged</u> their customers, _____

My teacher says that when you <u>miscount</u>, _____

You can easily <u>dehydrate</u> in hot weather, so _____

Sentence practice

Write <u>three</u> sentences to give instructions for cooking something from the freezer. Use some **verbs** with **prefixes**.

_____

_____

_____

Revision 2

1 Write the **adverb** that can be formed from the **adjective**. Then write a
sentence using the adverb you have made.

awkward   _____   _____

desperate   _____   _____

urgent   _____   _____

merry   _____   _____

2 Write the **plural** form of each word.

question   _____   scientist   _____

balcony   _____   ox   _____

address   _____   calf   _____

volcano   _____   salmon   _____

3 Complete each sentence with a **noun** formed from the verb in brackets.

Mum says she needs some rest and _____ while on holiday.   (relax)

I have an important _____ to make.   (announce)

The school secretary says we need a paper _____ in the office.   (shred)

4 What does the **prefix** 'inter–' mean in the **word family** below? Tick <u>one</u>.

> **interrupt   intervene   interfere   interface**

beneath ☐   between ☐   above ☐   below ☐

5 What does the **root** 'locus' mean in the **word family** below? Tick <u>one</u>.

> **local   location   locate   locomotive**

long ☐   time ☐   place ☐   live ☐

6 Complete each sentence below with a **compound noun**.

I saw a _____ in the garden.

We were playing in the _____ .

The teachers were drinking tea in the _____ .

7 Write a sentence using the word 'leak' as a **verb**.

_____

Write a sentence using the word 'leak' as a **noun**.

_____

8 Write a sentence using the word 'low' as an **adjective**.

_____

Write a sentence using the word 'low' as an **adverb**.

_____

9 Underline all the **adverbs** in the sentences below.

"It will soon be time to leave here," said the old man sadly.

Nadia told us later that she saw a fire engine suddenly pull up outside.

I have spent the money already and therefore we can't go to the cinema now.

10 Write a sentence for each **preposition** given below.

between _____

about _____

behind _____

through _____

after _____

on _____

Writing task 2

Read all about it!

You are a news reporter on a local newspaper. Your task is to write a short news story that will interest your readers. Choose an idea from the headlines below or use one of your own. You should report what happened in the style of a newspaper reporter.

Before you start writing, think about:

● what happened

● who was involved

● what your readers will want to know about the events

● how to make it sound like a news story

Use this space to write down some ideas.

Remember

- Think about the grammar and vocabulary you use.
- Use correct punctuation.
- Check your work carefully.

Read all about it!

Commas within sentences

Commas have a number of uses but they are always used <u>within</u> a sentence. They are used to show breaks between different parts of a sentence (for example, in **lists**, with **question tags**, in **direct speech**, in **parentheses** and after **fronted adverbials**). They can separate words, phrases or clauses.

"Dad, is that you?" I called into the darkness.
Then, out of the silence, I heard another creak. Someone, or something, was out there. Clutching the duvet, I huddled in bed.

Try it

1 Insert **commas** in the correct place(s) in each sentence.

"Come here " she said "and tell me again."

The sense of touch means I can feel if things are hot cold soft hard smooth or rough.

Carbohydrates such as starch and sugar give us energy.

Without warning the huge bird swooped down and grabbed him.

Wherever she went that day the cat seemed to follow her.

Have you been snowboarding before Emma?

2 Explain why a **comma** is used in each sentence.

I've told you this story before, haven't I?

_____

When the sun is high in the sky, there is nothing better than a picnic by the river.

_____

Poor Chris, who is allergic to cats, began to sneeze.

_____

Sentence practice

Write <u>two</u> sentences about someone going into a mysterious house. Use one or more **commas** in each sentence.

_____

_____

Commas to avoid ambiguity

Commas are important – sometimes they can change the meaning of a sentence.

Keep tackling Joe.   Keep tackling, Joe.

Commas make the meaning of a sentence clear and prevent any ambiguity or misunderstanding. Think what this sentence would mean without the comma!

The things I like best are cooking, my dog and music.

Try it

1 Explain how the **commas** change the meaning in each pair of sentences.

No tickets are available.   No, tickets are available.

_____

_____

Lola was a pretty smart girl.   Lola was a pretty, smart girl.

_____

_____

2 Rewrite each sentence using a **comma** to clarify the meaning.

After he ate the lion was full.   _____

I'm starving. Let's eat Mum.   _____

Above a seagull squawked loudly.   _____

To Callum James seemed bold.   _____

Are we going to paint Miss Jones?   _____

I like collecting sports and   _____

watching films.   _____

Sentence practice

Write <u>two</u> versions of a sentence to show how a **comma** can change the meaning.

_____

_____

Linking paragraphs using adverbials

Remember

You can use **paragraphs** to develop your ideas in a piece of writing. Linking **adverbials** can be used at the start of paragraphs to make it clear how your ideas fit together. This helps to give the text cohesion.

We would like to offer some suggestions to improve the school playground. Firstly, we would like you to consider providing new equipment. Secondly, we could set up a quiet area.

Try it

1. Underline the **adverbials** that show how each pair of ideas links together.

Outside the cabin, you can enjoy the woodland setting.
Inside, you will find a welcoming fire and everything you need.

To begin with, we will grow vegetables in pots and containers.
After that, we hope to have a small vegetable patch in the school grounds.

First of all, make sure that you have all the necessary safety equipment.
Secondly, check the weather forecast before you set out.

On the one hand, firework displays can be thrilling to watch.
On the other hand, many people are injured by fireworks every year.

2. Plan a piece of non-fiction writing with the title: 'Water is more precious than gold'. Write the <u>first</u> sentence for each **paragraph**, using **adverbials** to link your ideas.

Introduction: Water is definitely more precious than gold.

_____

_____

_____

_____

_____

Sentence practice

Make a plan for a piece of non-fiction writing, persuading people to support your favourite charity. Write the <u>first</u> sentence for each **paragraph**. Write your plan on a separate piece of paper.

Linking ideas within paragraphs

Within a **paragraph**, you need to show how the ideas link together, to make it clear and give it cohesion. You can use **adverbials** to show the links between sentences, and **pronouns** to refer back to previous ideas.

We could grow our own vegetables and then sell them. For example, we could grow tomatoes in pots or potatoes in sacks. This would not be too expensive.

Try it

1 Underline the **adverbials** and circle the **pronouns** that help to link the ideas between each pair of sentences.

The T-shirt is made of a special fabric that helps to keep you cool. In addition, this is very hard-wearing.

We have complained many times about the overflowing rubbish bins. They are still outside our school, however.

Anna Sewell's only book, Black Beauty, was published in 1878. Soon after that, she died, without knowing how successful it would be.

We found that children had different opinions about e-readers. Some, for example, liked the convenience of an e-reader, while others preferred an old-fashioned book.

2 Write a sentence to follow the given sentence. Use **adverbials** and/or **pronouns** to link the sentences together.

The park has facilities suitable for children of all ages. _____

_____

In some countries, large areas of rainforest have been destroyed. _____

_____

Some children may argue that they need their mobile phone in class. _____

_____

Sentence practice

Write a **paragraph** about an idea for an after-school club at your school. Use **adverbials** and **pronouns** to link your ideas together. Write the paragraph on a separate piece of paper.

Standard English: adverbs

> ### Remember
>
> Sometimes people use **adjectives** instead of **adverbs** when they speak. This is not **Standard English**. In writing, you should use adverbs to describe verbs or other adjectives.
>
> Zain <u>ran quick</u> in his race. ✗   Zain <u>ran quickly</u> in his race. ✓
> Jess <u>did good</u> to reach the final. ✗   Jess <u>did well</u> to reach the final. ✓
> Ben was in a <u>real difficult</u> heat. ✗   Ben was in a <u>really difficult</u> heat. ✓

Try it

1 Choose the word from the brackets that completes each sentence using **Standard English**.

_____, she reached the cliff edge just in time.   (lucky luckily)

We need to think _____ about this problem.   (seriously serious)

He dressed _____ for the occasion.   (smart smartly)

The parrot squawked _____ all morning.   (loud loudly)

They played _____ in the first half.   (well good)

The deafening roar lessened _____.   (gradually gradual)

2 Rewrite each sentence using the **Standard English** form of all words.

She done it beautiful.   _____

The wind blowed real gentle.   _____

The concert were well good.   _____

I tries to eat healthy.   _____

It were a fair big mistake.   _____

I should have writ the note proper.   _____

Sentence practice

Write a sentence using the **adjective** 'terrible', and a sentence using the **adverb** formed from it.

adjective   _____

adverb   _____

Sentence adverbs

Remember

Adverbs are used to add detail about how, where, when or how often events happen. However, you can also use adverbs to add a comment on a whole sentence. These adverbs are often fronted, or placed at the start of the sentence.

Fortunately, Mum was delayed by bad traffic.
Surprisingly, she didn't notice the mess.

Try it

1   Complete each sentence using a suitable **adverb** from the box. Punctuate it correctly.

amazingly   interestingly   sadly   surprisingly   unfortunately

_____ the next day the cupboard was full again.

_____ a number of paintings have been damaged in the flood.

_____ people could not tell the difference between the two ice creams.

_____ he was too ill to go to Sunil's party.

_____ it sometimes snows even in spring.

2   Complete each sentence, using the given **adverb** to comment or add meaning.

Luckily, _____

Strangely, _____

Obviously, _____

Incredibly, _____

Curiously, _____

Personally, _____

Sentence practice

Write <u>two</u> sentences, one to introduce a problem and one about solving the problem. Use the **adverbs** 'unfortunately' and 'fortunately'.

_____

_____

Word classes

Remember

Some words belong to more than one **word class**, depending on how they are used in the sentence. For example, 'before' can be either a **conjunction** (before a clause) or a **preposition** (before a phrase).

I left before it finished. (conjunction)   I left before the end. (preposition)

Similarly, 'her' can be either a **pronoun** or a **determiner**.

I see her every day. (pronoun)   I see her friend every day. (determiner)

Try it

1   **Read each sentence. Is the underlined word a conjunction or a preposition?**

We went for a walk <u>since</u> the sun was shining.   _____

I have not seen Jade <u>since</u> nine o'clock this morning.   _____

Let's keep going <u>until</u> the car runs out of petrol.   _____

You will stay here <u>until</u> the end of time.   _____

Read each sentence. Is the underlined word a determiner or a pronoun?

Mum gave me these grapes but I already had <u>some</u> at lunchtime.   _____

I saw <u>some</u> lovely clothes in the shops on Saturday.   _____

Put <u>those</u> red apples in the bowl over there.   _____

Would you like to try <u>those</u> on?   _____

2   **Write a sentence using 'after' as a conjunction. Then use it as a preposition.**

conjunction   _____

preposition   _____

Write a sentence using 'this' as a determiner. Then use it as a pronoun.

determiner   _____

pronoun   _____

Sentence practice

Write a sentence using 'before' as a conjunction and 'these' as a pronoun.

_____

Possessives

A possessive can be a **possessive noun** (a noun followed by 'apostrophe s') or a **possessive pronoun**. Possessive pronouns stand alone instead of a noun.

the planet's future   (possessive noun)
environmentalists' concerns   (plural possessive noun)
the choice is ours   (possessive pronoun)

Try it

1 Rewrite each phrase as a **possessive noun**. Use an **apostrophe**.

the generosity shown by the public   _____

an announcement made by the Prime Minister   _____

impossible deeds performed by our heroes   _____

the biography about Martin Luther King   _____

the study carried out by scientists   _____

the courage shown by the women   _____

2 Rewrite each sentence using a **possessive pronoun**.

She came up with the idea.   _____

The mistake was made by me.   _____

It is our responsibility.   _____

You have to make the decision.   _____

They have broken the world record. _____

He gave the best performance.   _____

Sentence practice

Write <u>three</u> sentences about opinions. Use a **possessive noun** or **possessive pronoun** in each.

_____

_____

_____

More relative clauses

Relative clauses usually give more information about a noun. However, some relative clauses refer to what is said in the whole of the **main clause**, rather than to just a noun. These relative clauses are separated from the main clause by a **comma**.

Edmund Hillary and Sherpa Tenzing were the first to reach the summit of Everest, <u>which was a remarkable achievement</u>.

Try it

1 Underline the **relative clause** in each sentence. Tick the box if the relative clause refers to the whole **clause**, rather than the **noun**.

There was no-one in the swimming pool, which was weird. ☐

I fed the kittens, which were only a few weeks old. ☐

In August we are going to India, which I am very excited about. ☐

Something startled the creature, which gave Beth the chance to escape. ☐

The painting, which is very old, is above the fireplace in the dining room. ☐

We chose Ethan, which was a mistake, and Evie to complete our team. ☐

2 Add a **relative clause** that refers to the **main clause**. Punctuate each sentence correctly.

We played our first league game last week _____

The fire is spreading through the forest _____

A wolf howled in the distance _____

The house is very old _____

Connor helped the man with his bags _____

There was a lot of shouting in the garden _____

Sentence practice

Write <u>two</u> sentences about something bad happening. In both sentences, use a **relative clause** that refers to events in the **main clause**.

_____

Conditional sentences

A **conditional sentence** is a sentence in which one thing depends on another. It has a **main clause** and a **subordinate clause**. The subordinate clause starts with a **conjunction** such as 'if' or 'unless', and states the 'condition' needed for the event in the main clause to happen.

We should be there by ten if we leave at nine o'clock.
If the weather is fine, we will do lots of outdoor activities.
The trip will go ahead unless the weather is really bad.

Try it

1 Underline the **subordinate clause** that gives the condition in each sentence.

If the weather improves, we could visit the coast this weekend.

I won't set the people free unless you promise to help me.

If we can persuade someone famous to open our summer fair, lots of people will come.

My little brother won't go swimming unless I go with him.

If you listen to a lot of loud music, it can damage your ears.

Our planet will not survive unless we take care of it.

2 Rewrite each sentence, adding a **subordinate clause** that gives a condition.

Superman will save the planet.

_____

I can raise a lot of money for this important charity.

_____

The crops will fail and people will starve.

_____

Sentence practice

You are going to the beach at the weekend. Write <u>three</u> **conditional** sentences about what you might do.

_____

_____

Revision 3

1 Underline all the **pronouns** in the sentence.

Dad said I should save up and buy the
game myself if I want it so badly.

2 Underline the **pronoun** in each sentence and write the **nouns** they refer to.

All birds have wings, although some cannot fly.   _____

All birds have beaks and they use these to find food.   _____ _____

Many children love sweets and they often buy them.   _____ _____

Amy has lost her pen. Tell her if you see it.   _____ _____

Sean has a new green jacket. It really suits him.   _____ _____

3 Rewrite each sentence using the **past perfect verb form** rather than the
simple past tense.

The pond froze overnight.   _____

The ship sank in the storm.   _____

I wrote to the council.   _____

She tore the paper in half.   _____

4 Rewrite each sentence, changing it from indirect speech to **direct speech**.

Amina said my dancing was absolutely amazing.

_____

Imran asked if I had found the secret key.

_____

5 Insert the missing **punctuation** in these examples of **direct speech**.

You will be safe here said the young girl until the morning

The doctor said I think you should stay home from school today

I have made you many gifts said the cunning goldsmith Edwin will
show them to you

It's lovely and sunny outside said Dad I'm going for a walk by
the river

6 Underline all the **determiners** in the sentences below.

There is one banana and some grapes left in the fruit bowl but no apples.

Your friend has two sisters, I have three brothers and you have a twin.

Can you see the difference between this picture and that picture?

7 Add a different **determiner** to each **noun**.

_____ actor   _____ fabric   _____ desks

_____ music   _____ computer   _____ geese

_____ traffic   _____ factories   _____ hair

8 Make each **noun** into an expanded **noun phrase** by adding a **determiner**, **adjectives** and a **prepositional phrase**.

lizard   _____

sword   _____

stadium   _____

corridor   _____

9 Use the **pronouns** 'I' and 'me' to correctly complete the sentences below.

Greg told Belle and _____ where he was going.

Katie and _____ are going to the cinema after school.

Mum made cheese-and-pickle sandwiches for Ben and _____ .

I think Prashin and _____ might make a model castle.

10 Complete each sentence using a different **modal verb**.

The kite _____ blow away in this wind.

We _____ go to the coffee shop later.

I _____ need a rest soon.

You _____ get a mountain bike for your birthday.

You _____ not stay up too late.

Writing task 3

Save it!

A place near where you live is under threat from developers. You want to save it. You could choose an idea from the pictures or one of your own. Your task is to write a letter or flier explaining why it should be saved and persuading other people to agree with you.

Before you start writing, think about:

- the details of the place
- the reasons why it should be saved
- what you want other people to do
- how you will sound convincing

Use this space to write down some ideas.

Remember

- Think about the grammar and vocabulary you use.
- Use correct punctuation.
- Check your work carefully.

Save it!

_____

_____

_____

_____

_____

_____

_____

_____

_____

_____

_____

_____

_____

_____

_____

_____

_____

_____

_____

_____

_____

_____

_____

Progress chart

Tick the circle when you can do what the statement says.

Section 1

○ I can use fronted adverbials to add detail and for effect.

○ I can use fronted subordinate clauses with a range of conjunctions.

○ I can punctuate direct speech correctly.

○ I can explain the use of pronouns and identify different types (personal, possessive, relative).

○ I can reword a sentence to make pronouns clear.

○ I can use verb forms that need auxiliary verbs (progressive, perfect form).

○ I can correct non-Standard use of pronouns and write in Standard English.

○ I can recognise double negatives and reword sentences to avoid them.

Section 2

○ I can recognise and use a range of determiners to specify nouns.

○ I can use expanded noun phrases to describe and give detail about nouns.

○ I can write relative clauses beginning with 'who'/'that'/'which'/'whose' or 'where'/'when'.

○ I can use brackets, dashes or commas to show a parenthesis.

○ I can use adverbs or modal verbs to show different levels of possibility.

○ I can change nouns or adjectives into verbs using suffixes (e.g. –ate, –ise).

○ I can use prefixes (e.g. dis–, mis–, over–) to change the meaning of verbs.

Section 3

○ I can use commas to separate phrases and clauses within a sentence.

○ I can use commas to clarify the meaning of a sentence.

○ I can use a range of adverbials to link ideas across paragraphs.

○ I can use adverbials, conjunctions and pronouns to link ideas in paragraphs.

○ I can recognise non-Standard use of adverbs and use the Standard forms.

○ I can use sentence adverbs to comment on a sentence.

○ I can identify conjunctions/prepositions and pronouns/determiners by how they are used.

○ I can use possessive pronouns and apostrophes to show possession.

○ I can write relative clauses that refer to a whole clause rather than a noun.

○ I can write conditional sentences using conjunctions such as 'if' or 'unless'.